Who Do You See?

A Rain Forest Rap

by Laura Layton Strom

Who do you see?
Who do you see?

Who do you see
way up **in** that tree?

I see a monkey
eating fruit.

He's swinging free
in his hairy suit.

I see a sloth.
I see him creep.

He barely moves.
Look! He's asleep!

Who do you see?
Who do you see?

Who do you see way **above** that tree?

I see a toucan
with a bright orange beak.

That beak's a cool tool
any day of the week.

Who do you see?
Who do you see?

Who do you see
way **under** that tree?

I see a croc
with scaly gray skin.

He is looking for frogs.
Watch that great big grin!

Who can you see?